This Walker book belongs to:

Ayo

Text first published 1985
by HarperCollins Publishers Ltd
First published in 1994
by Walker Books Ltd
87 Vauxhall Walk
London SE11 5HJ

This edition first published 2008

2 4 6 8 10 9 7 5 3 1

This book has been typeset in Garamond Book Educational.

Printed in China

British Library Cataloguing in Publication Data:
a catalogue record for this book is available.
from the British Library

ISBN 978-1-4063-1667-4

www.walkerbooks.co.uk

by

Judy Hindley

Illustrated by

Nick Sharratt

WALKER BOOKS
AND SUBSIDIARIES
LONDON · BOSTON · SYDNEY · AUCKLAND

Animals marching one by one.

The elephant played

on a thundering drum:

One by one by one…

Count them!

One by one by one…

2

Animals marching two by two,

ostriches following kangaroos.

I think they escaped from

a neighbouring zoo.

Did you escape from the zoo, too?

Two by two by two…

3

Animals marching three by three,

arriving as far as the eye can see.

Two for you and one for me.

Three by three by three…

Animals marching four by four,

more and more and more and more.

Shut the door!

Don't let them in!

Four by four by four…

And now there are animals five by five –

Snakes alive! They're beginning to jive!

Five by five by five…

And here come another lot.

Isn't it six?

Close the windows – quick!

What if they come to our house?

Too many for dinner! Too many for tea!

Too many for you!

Too much for me!

Six by six by six...

7

And now they're arriving

seven by seven.

Oh, good heaven! Seven by seven!

Seven by seven by seven...

Animals marching eight by eight,

some of them early and some of them late,

but all coming round at a terrible rate,

running and jumping and jiving and

sliding and circling round our house –

Look!

Stop them, quick! Before it's too late!

Eight by eight by eight…

9

And now they're travelling

nine by nine.

There seem to be more of them

all of the time!

Nine by nine by nine…

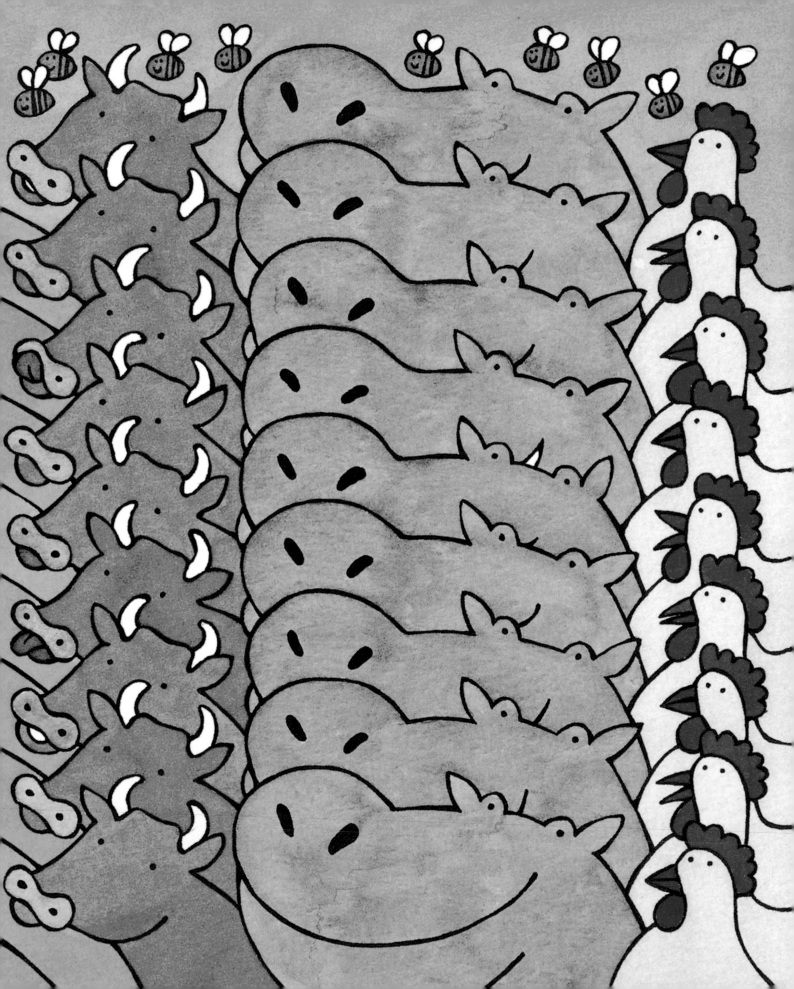

Animals marching ten by ten

SURROUNDED

our house.

And what happened then?

We said,

"You can all go home now."

And the animals all went back again…

Ten

by nine

by eight

by seven

by six

by five

by four

by three

by two…

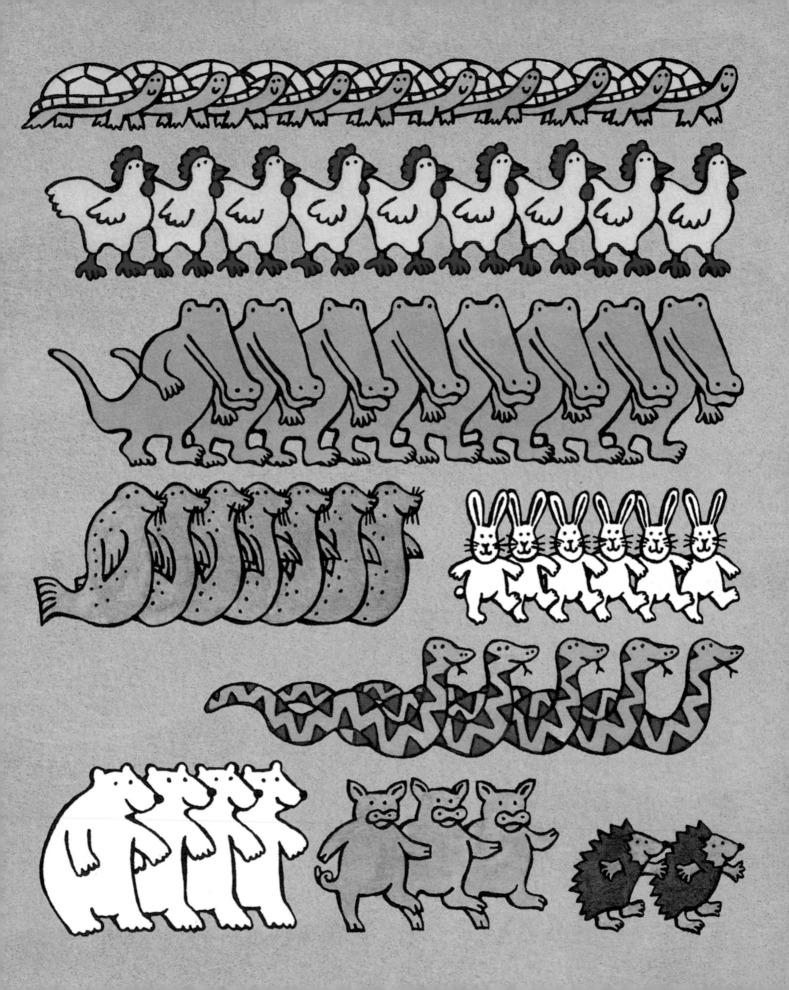

but we let the last one stay.

Titles in this series

ISBN 978-1-4063-1669-8

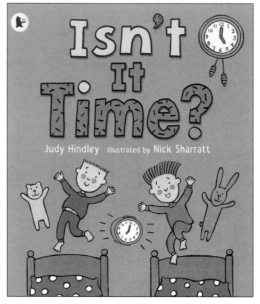

ISBN 978-1-4063-1670-4

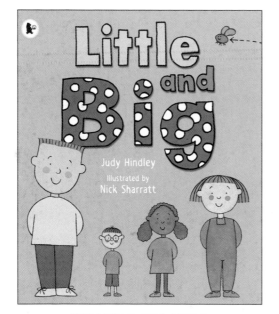

ISBN 978-1-4063-1668-1

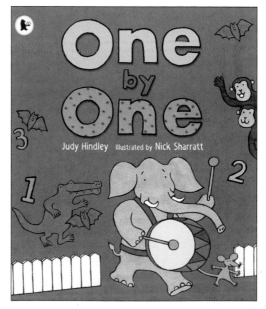

ISBN 978-1-4063-1667-4

Available from all good bookstores

www.walkerbooks.co.uk